9

This Book
Belongs to

Mariam

FIELD POPPIES © by Gay Corran 1987

A RAINBOW in the MORNING

poetry and prose to
celebrate the year

A RAINBOW in the MORNING

——— ✳ ———

*poetry and prose to
celebrate the year*

COMPILED BY FIONA WATERS
ILLUSTRATED BY PAULA CLOONAN

Blackie

For Fee, with much love

This selection copyright © 1991 Fiona Waters
Illustrations © 1991 Paula Cloonan
First published 1991 by Blackie and Son Ltd

A CIP catalogue record for this book
is available from the British Library.

ISBN 0 216 92863 X

Blackie and Son Ltd
7 Leicester Place
London WC2H 7BP

Printed in Hong Kong by Wing King Tong Co. Ltd.

A rainbow in the morning is the shepherd's warning,
A rainbow at night is the shepherd's delight.

JANUARY

If the birds begin to sing in January,
Frosts are on the way.

The Snowdrops

'Where are the snowdrops?' said the sun.
  'Dead!' said the frost,
'Buried and lost
  Every one!'

'A foolish answer,' said the sun:
  'They did not die,
Asleep they lie
  Every one!'

'And I will wake them, I, the sun,
  Into the light,
All clad in white
  Every one!'

ANNIE MATHESON

A New, Clear Winter

For three days
drifts have cut off the village.
No mail or newspapers,
the shop short of supplies,
cars like igloos.
Obese in layers of coats
I stumped knee-deep through snow
beyond the last farm
and along a submerged road
where hedges have vanished.

A stark study:
grey sky, white fields,
the black, distant wood.
Not a single bird,
not a semi-colon of colour.
The wind is shivering
itself into silence.
In the numbed air
of a new, clear winter
only my eyes move.

A nuclear winter
could be similarly viewed:
fields deep in white ash,
charred woodland,
the sun hibernating
in a thick, grey blanket,
and overall an absence
of breathing, a silence,
and the last human,
stump-like, numb.

WES MAGEE

Kings of Orient

We three kings of Orient are;
Bearing gifts we traverse afar
Field and fountain, moor and mountain,
Following yonder star:

O star of wonder, star of night,
Star with royal beauty bright,
Westward leading, still proceeding,
Guide us to thy perfect light.

MELCHIOR
Born a king on Bethlehem plain,
Gold I bring, to crown him again –
King for ever, ceasing never,
Over us all to reign:

CASPAR

Frankincense to offer have I;
Incense owns a Deity nigh:
Prayer and praising, all men raising,
Worship him, God most high:

BALTHAZAR

Myrrh is mine; its bitter perfume
Breathes a life of gathering gloom;
Sorrowing, sighing, bleeding, dying,
Sealed in the stone-cold tomb:

Glorious now, behold him arise,
King and God, and sacrifice!
Heaven sings alleluya,
Alleluya the earth replies:

JOHN HENRY HOPKINS

Giant Winter

Giant Winter preys on the earth,
Gripping with talons of ice,
Squeezing, seeking a submission,
Tightening his grip like a vice.

Starved of sunlight shivering trees
Are bent by his torturing breath.
The seeds burrow into the soil
Preparing to fight to the death.

Giant Winter sneers at their struggles,
Blows blizzards from his frozen jaws,
Ripples cold muscles of iron,
Clenches tighter his icicle claws.

Just as he seems to be winning,
Strength suddenly ebbs from his veins.
He releases his hold and collapses.
Giant Spring gently takes up the reins.

Snarling, bitter with resentment,
Winter crawls to his polar den,
Where he watches and waits till it's time
To renew the battle again.

JOHN FOSTER

FEBRUARY

February fill dyke, black or white★

★ This means that regardless of rain or snow the ditches will usually fill during February.

Charm for St Valentine's Eve

On going to bed, place your shoes in the form of a letter T, and repeat the following verse. Then reverse the shoes, and say three times more.

> I place my shoes like a letter T,
> In hopes my true love I shall see,
> In his apparel and his array,
> As he is now and every day.

ANON

First Sight

Lambs that learn to walk in snow
When their bleating clouds the air
Meet a vast unwelcome, know
Nothing but a sunless glare.
Newly stumbling to and fro
All they find, outside the fold,
Is a wretched width of cold.

As they wait beside the ewe,
Her fleeces wetly caked, there lies
Hidden round them, waiting too,
Earth's immeasurable surprise.
They could not grasp it if they knew,
What so soon will wake and grow
Utterly unlike the snow.

PHILIP LARKIN

The Invaders

Today it is snowing.
The starlings are out in force
Bullying the sparrows,
Their bayonet beaks
Commandeering the breadcrumbs.
Like stormtroopers
They take over the garden,
Asserting that might means right.

JOHN FOSTER

The Gospel According to St Luke

Lord, now lettest thou thy servant depart in peace, according
to thy word:
For mine eyes have seen thy salvation,
Which thou hast prepared before the face of all people:
A light to lighten the Gentiles, and the glory of thy people
Israel.

CHAPTER 2, VERSES 29-32

from *Tom's Midnight Garden*

That winter the frost had begun at the end of December and went on – with a milder spell for a week in January – to the beginning of March. It was of the greatest severity. Even running waters froze at last. Ice stopped the wheels of the upriver water-mills, and blocked the way for the barges that, in those days, plied from King's Lynn as far upstream as the hithes of Castleford.

The frost was over all England. On some waters oxen were roasted whole, as though that proved what a fine frost this was, and what ice was best used for. On the Cherwell, at Oxford, a coach with six horses was driven down the middle of the frozen river, to the great satisfaction of all concerned. But the people of Castleford and the Fens knew the truest and greatest and best use of ice: they skated.

There had been skating on the river for several weeks when Tom and Hatty came down to it; and it seemed to them as if there must be more people skating than could possibly be doing market-day business in the town.

Not everyone skated well or fast: there were some learners, and a policeman who moved with the dignified pace of a navy-blue swan. There was also the newer fashion of skating – figure-skating: Hatty pointed it out to Tom. In one place an orange had been set centrally upon the ice, and four top-hatted, dignified gentlemen were describing a harmony of figures to it – from it – round it. Suddenly a town-urchin, on rusty Fen runners, partly strapped, partly tied with string to his boots, dashed in, snatched up the orange and dashed away again with his teeth already in it. The swaying, shifting crowd of skaters closed up behind him, and the figure-skating gentlemen stopped skating, and were extremely annoyed.

Like Tom, Hatty laughed aloud at the impudence of the theft; but all time she was looking round her sharply and a little nervously. Among all the townspeople and countrypeople, someone might recognize her, and pass comment on her being there alone. However, Hatty was fortunate: no one seemed to notice her at all.

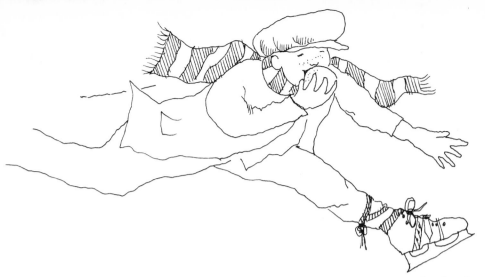

The skates were on, and now Hatty and Tom were ready for the ice: two skaters on one pair of skates, which seemed to Tom both the eeriest and the most natural thing in the world. A new skill and power came into him, as though these skates knew their work better than the skater: he could skate as well as Hatty, because he had her skates. The only difference between them was that his blades left no cut or bruise upon the surface of the ice in travelling over it.

They did not skate with linked hands, as many skating partners did, for fear of the odd appearance being noticed; but, once they had left behind the thick crowds of sociable skaters just below the town, they skated abreast, keeping time together, stroke for stroke. There was no wind at all that afternoon, and they cut through the still air faster and faster.

Hatty had pinned her skirt up above her ankles, for greater freedom of movement; and now she abandoned the use of her muff, the better to swing her arms in time with their skating. Their speed made the muff fly out behind her, on its cord, and at last a stroke gave it such a violent fling that the cord broke and the fur ball of the muff shot away and landed in the middle of a game of bandy and somehow became part of the game, and was never seen again. Hatty saw it disappear, and neither stopped nor faltered in her course, but only laughed, as though she cared nothing now for muffs or improprieties or aunts. They skated on.

PHILLIPA PEARCE

First Primrose

I saw it in the lane
One morning going to school
After a soaking night of rain,
The year's first primrose,
Lying there familiar and cool
In its private place
Where little else grows
Beneath dripping hedgerows,
Stalk still wet, face
Pale as Inca gold,
Spring glistening in every delicate fold.
I knelt down by the roadside there,
Caught the faint whiff of its shy scent
On the cold and public air,
Then got up and went
On my slow way,
Glad and grateful I'd seen
The first primrose that day,
Half yellow, half green.

LEONARD CLARK

MARCH

If March comes in like a lion,
It goes out like a lamb.
If it comes in like a lamb,
It goes out like a lion.

Beachcomber

Monday I found a boot –
Rust and salt leather.
I gave it back to the sea, to dance in.

Tuesday a spar of timber worth thirty bob.
Next winter
It will be a chair, a coffin, a bed.

Wednesday a half can of Swedish spirits.
I tilted my head.
The shore was cold with mermaids and angels.

Thursday I got nothing, seaweed,
A whale bone,
Wet feet and a loud cough.

Friday I held a seaman's skull,
Sand spilling from it
The way time is told on kirkyard stones.

Saturday a barrel of sodden oranges.
A Spanish ship
Was wrecked last month at The Kame.

Sunday, for fear of the elders,
I sit on my bum.
What's heaven? A sea chest with
                    a thousand gold coins.

GEORGE MACKAY BROWN

The Nature Lesson

The teacher has the flowers on her desk,
Then goes round, giving one to each of us.
We are going to study the primrose –
To find out all about it. It has five petals,
Notice the little dent in each, making it heart-shaped
And a pale green calyx (And O! the hairy stem!).
Now, in the middle of the flower
There may be a little knob – that is the pistil –
Or perhaps your flower may show the bunch of stamens.
 We look at our flowers
To find out which kind we have got.

Now we are going to look inside,
So pull your petals off, one by one.
 But wait . . .
If I pull my flowers to pieces it will stop
Being a primrose. It will be just bits
Strewn on my desk. I can't pull it to pieces.
What does it matter what goes on inside?
I won't find out by pulling it to pieces,
Because it will not be a primrose any more,
And the bits will not mean anything at all.
A primrose is a primrose, not just bits.

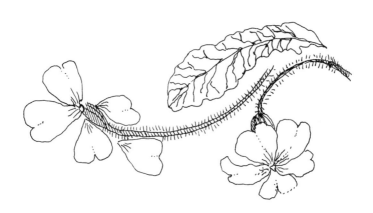

It lies there, a five-petalled primrose,
A whole primrose, a living primrose.
To find out what is inside I make it dead,
And then it will not be a primrose.
You can't find out
What goes on inside a living flower that way.
The teacher talks, fingers rustle . . .
I will look over my neighbour's flower
And leave my primrose whole. But if the teacher comes
And tells me singly to pull my flower to pieces
Then I will do as I am told. The teacher comes,
Passes my neighbour on her gangway side,
Does not see my primrose is still whole,
Goes by, not noticing, nobody notices.
My flower remains a primrose, that they all
Want to find out about by pulling to pieces.
I am alone: all the world is alone
In the flower left breathing on my desk.

MARJORIE BALDWIN

from *The Little Grey Men*

It was one of those days at the tail end of the winter when spring, in some subtle way, announced its presence. The hedges were still purple and bristly, the fields bleached and bitten, full of quarrelling starling flocks; but there was no doubt about it, the winter was virtually over and done with for another seven months. The great tide was on the turn, to creep so slowly at first and then to rise ever higher to culminate in the glorious flood, the top of the tide, at midsummer.

Think of it! All that power, all those millions of leaves, those extra inches to be added to bushes, trees and flowers. It was all there under the earth, though you would never have guessed it.

After a soft grey morning, the sun had slowly broken through the clouds, and every blackbird and thrush in Lucking's Meadow began to warble and tune up; the first opening bars of a great symphony in praise of Life.

The willow bush by the Folly brook showed silver buttons up every slender wand and on the rough grey bark of the leaning oak tree on the other side of the pool three sleepy flies were sidling about, enjoying the warm rays.

At this spot, for some reason known only to itself, the Folly brook turned at a right angle.

Beneath the oak the water had washed away the sandy bank, and many winter floods had laid bare some of the massive hawser roots which projected in a twisted tangle from the soil of the bank. The sun, shining full on the steep bluff, threw shadows from the over-hanging roots, so that underneath all was darkness.

Close to the margin of the glittering water, there was a miniature beach of coloured shingle and white sand; and from the glare on the stream, wavering bars of reflected light played to and fro on the bulging trunk of the oak. These light bars moved up and down in ripples, fading away when the sun was dimmed for an instant by a passing cloud.

27

It had been a dry winter and the Folly brook was running fresh and clear, higher than in summer, of course, but quite undimmed by floodcloud. It was so clear that near the beach every stone and pebble on the bottom could be seen, though where the water was deeper, all was tawny obscurity, the colour of ripe old ale.

Near the bank, the tangled reeds were as white as bleached bone, though if you had looked more closely, sharp green sword points could have been seen just beginning to pierce the dead vegetation. Later these reeds formed a deep green thicket, the strong juicy blades growing so close together that only a water-vole could slip between. The bank on the side opposite to the oak shelved gradually to the water's edge, and here Farmer Lucking's cattle came to drink. They had poached and punched the soil at the 'marge' until it was in an awful mess and the grass for some way up the bank was quite worn away. But in the stream itself there was little mud, for the bottom was hard sand and shingle. Most of the mud which the heavy stolid beasts had collected to their knees was soon washed off by the current if they stood long enough in the stream.

Something moved in the shadow under the root. At first you might have thought it was a water-rat or a mouse; then, if you had waited long enough, keeping very still (for the Little People usually know when any mortal is about) you might have been lucky enough to see Baldmoney. He came out from under the root very slowly, peeping first one way and then another, listening.

BB

In March

At winter's end when hungry foxes sleep
A few uneasy hours in earthy dens,
And shivering hares squat in their forms, and sheep
At lambing time bed down in farmyard pens;
Then stiff with cold in secret garden holes
Thin dormice lie, curled up with drowsy moles.

Before the frosty darkness falls outside,
There flit on faintly coloured wing a pair
Of chaffinches who on the branches hide,
For they have found a quiet lodging where
They, too, can settle down this night and rest,
And in the morning start to build their nest.

And in the farmhouse now our yawning cat,
After a busy day begins to tire,
And lies there warm and sleek and fat,
Stretched out beside the blazing kitchen fire;
Dreaming and purring she is well away,
It is the ending of a chill March day.

So wild and tame have skies about their heads
Where all the stars of early springtime shine.
They go contented to their peaceful beds,
And I am full of sleep and go to mine.

LEONARD CLARK

APRIL

When April blows his horn
'Tis good for hay and corn.★

★ The 'horn' is a reference to thunder. If good hay and corn are promised, it also
means a fine summer.

The Lent Lily

'Tis spring; come out to ramble
  The hilly brakes around,
For under thorn and bramble
  About the hollow ground
  The primroses are found.

And there's the windflower chilly
  With all the winds at play,
And there's the Lenten lily
  That has not long to stay
  And dies on Easter day.

And since till girls go maying
  You find the primroses still,
And find the windflower playing
  With every wind at will,
  But not the daffodil,

Bring baskets now, and sally
  Upon the spring's array,
And bear from hill and valley
  The daffodil away
  That dies on Easter day.

A E HOUSMAN

Under Milk Wood

To begin at the beginning:

It is spring, moonless night in the small town, starless and bible-black, the cobblestreets silent and the hunched, courters'-and-rabbits' wood limping invisible down to the sloeblack, slow, black, crowblack, fishingboat-bobbing sea. The houses are blind as moles (though moles see fine to-night in the snouting, velvet dingles) or blind as Captain Cat there in the muffled middle by the pump and the town clock, the shops in mourning, the Welfare Hall in widows' weeds. And all the people of the lulled and dumbfound town are sleeping now.

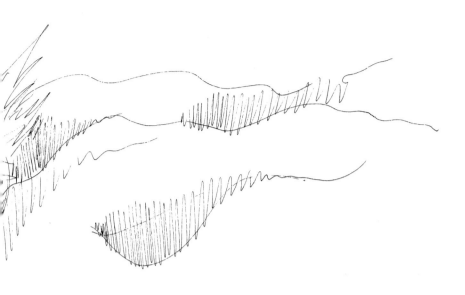

Hush, the babies are sleeping, the farmers, the fishers, the trades-
men and pensioners, cobbler, school-teacher, postman and publican,
the undertaker and the fancy woman, drunkard, dressmaker,
preacher, policeman, the webfoot cocklewomen and the tidy wives.
Young girls lie bedded soft or glide in their dreams, with rings and
trousseaux, bridesmaided by glow-worms down the aisles of the
organplaying wood. The boys are dreaming wicked or of the buck-
ing ranches of the night and the jollyrodgered sea. And the anthracite
statues of the horses sleep in the fields, and the cows in the byres, and
the dogs in the wetnosed yards; and the cats nap in the slant corners
or lope sly, streaking and needling, on the one cloud of the roofs.

You can hear the dew falling, and the hushed town breathing.
Only your eyes are unclosed to see the black and folded town fast,
and slow, asleep. And you alone can hear the invisible starfall, the
darkest-before-dawn minutely dewgrazed stir of the black, dab-filled
sea where the Arethusa, the Curlew and the Skylark, Zanzibar
Rhiannon, the Rover, the Cormorant, and the Star of Wales tilt and
ride.

Listen. It is night moving in the streets, the processional salt slow musical wind in Coronation Street and Cockle Row, it is the grass growing on Llaregyb Hill, dewfall, starfall, the sleep of birds in Milk Wood.

Listen. It is night in the chill, squat chapel, hymning in bonnet and brooch and bombazine black, butterfly choker and bootlace bow, coughing like nannygoats, sucking mintoes, fortywinking hallelujah; night in the four-ale, quiet as a domino; in Ocky Milkman's lofts like a mouse with gloves; in Dai Bread's bakery flying like black flour. It is tonight in Donkey Street, trotting silent, with seaweed on its hooves, along the cocked cobbles, past curtained fernpot, text and trinket, harmonium, holy dresser, watercolours done by hand, china dog and rosy tin tea-caddy. It is night neddying among the snuggeries of babies.

Look. It is night, dumbly, royally winding through the Coronation cherry trees; going through the graveyard of Bethesda with
winds gloved and folded, and dew doffed; tumbling by the Sailors
Arms.

Time passes. Listen. Time passes.

Come closer now.

Only you can hear the houses sleeping in the streets in the slow
deep salt and silent black, bandaged night. Only you can see, in the
blinded bedrooms, the combs and petticoats over the chairs, the jugs
and basins, the glasses of teeth, Thou Shalt Not on the wall, and the
yellowing dickybird-watching pictures of the dead. Only you can
hear and see, behind the eyes of the sleepers, the movements and
countries and mazes and colours and dismays and rainbows and
tunes and wishes and flight and fall and despairs and big seas of their
dreams.

From where you are, you can hear their dreams.

DYLAN THOMAS

35

The Wood Fire (a fragment)

'This is a brightsome blaze you've lit, good friend, to-night!'
'– Aye, it has been the bleakest spring I have felt for years,
And nought compares with cloven logs to keep alight:
I buy them bargain-cheap of the executioners,
As I dwell near; and they wanted the crosses out of sight
By Passover, not to affront the eyes of visitors.

'Yes, they're from the crucifixions last week-ending
At Kranion. We can sometimes use the poles again,
But they get split by the nails, and 'tis quicker work than
     mending
To knock together new; though the uprights now and then
Serve twice when they're let stand. But if a feast's impending,
As lately, you've to tidy up for the comers' ken.

'Though only three were impaled, you may know it didn't pass
     off
So quietly as was wont? That Galilee carpenter's son
Who boasted he was king, incensed the rabble to scoff:
I heard the noise from my garden. This piece is the one he was
     on . . .
Yes, it blazes up well if lit with a few dry chips and shroff;
And it's worthless for much else, what with cuts and stains
     thereon.'

THOMAS HARDY

from *The Secret Garden*

On that first morning when the sky was blue again Mary wakened very early. The sun was pouring in slanting rays through the blinds and there was something so joyous in the sight of it that she jumped out of bed and ran to the window. She drew up the blinds and opened the window itself and a great waft of fresh, scented air blew in upon her. The moor was blue and the whole world looked as if something Magic had happened to it. There were tender little fluting sounds here and there and everywhere, as if scores of birds were beginning to tune up for a concert. Mary put her hand out of the window and held it in the sun.

'It's warm – warm!' she said. 'It will make the green points push up and up and up, and it will make the bulbs and roots work and struggle with all their might under the earth.'

She kneeled down and leaned out of the window as far as she could, breathing big breaths and sniffing the air until she laughed because she remembered what Dickon's mother had said about the end of his nose quivering like a rabbit's.

'It must be very early,' she said. 'The little clouds are all pink and I've never seen the sky look like this. No one is up. I don't even hear the stable boys.'

A sudden thought made her scramble to her feet.

'I can't wait! I am going to see the garden!'

She had learnt to dress herself by this time and she put on her clothes in five minutes. She knew a small side door which she could unbolt herself and she flew downstairs in her stocking feet and put on her shoes in the hall. She unchained and unbolted and unlocked and when the door was open she sprang across the step with one bound, and there she was standing on the grass, which seemed to have turned green, and with the sun pouring down on her and warm sweet wafts about her and the fluting and twittering and singing coming from every bush and tree. She clasped her hands for pure joy and looked up in the sky and it was so blue and pink and pearly and white and flooded with springtime light that she felt as if she must flute and sing aloud herself and knew that thrushes and robins and skylarks could not possibly help it. She ran around the shrubs and paths towards the secret garden.

'It is all different already,' she said. 'The grass is greener and things are sticking up everywhere and things are uncurling and green buds of leaves are showing. This afternoon I am sure Dickon will come.'

The long warm rain had done strange things to the herbaceous beds which bordered the walk by the lower wall. There were things sprouting and pushing out from the roots of clumps of plants and there were actually here and there glimpses of royal purple and yellow unfurling among the stems of crocuses. Six months before Mistress Mary would not have seen how the world was waking up, but now she missed nothing.

When she had reached the place where the door hid itself under the ivy, she was startled by a curious loud sound. It was the caw-caw of a crow and it came from the top of the wall, and when she looked up, there sat a big glossy-plumaged blue-black bird, looking down at her very wisely indeed. She had never seen a crow so close before and he made her a little nervous, but the next moment he spread his wings and flapped away across the garden. She hoped he was not going to stay inside and she pushed the door open wondering if he would. When she got fairly into the garden she saw that he probably did intend to stay because he had alighted on a dwarf apple tree, and under the apple tree was lying a little reddish animal with a bushy tail, and both of them were watching the stooping body and rust-red head of Dickon, who was kneeling on the grass working hard.

FRANCES HODGSON BURNETT

MAY

A wet May,
Brings a good load of hay. ★

★ This means plenty of sun in June.

Flying Crooked

The butterfly, a cabbage-white,
(His honest idiocy of flight)
Will never now, it is too late,
Master the art of flying straight,
Yet has – who knows so well as I? –
A just sense of how not to fly:
He lurches here and here by guess
And God and hope and hopelessness.
Even the aerobatic swift
Has not his flying-crooked gift.

ROBERT GRAVES

A dry May and a rainy June
Puts the farmer's pipe in tune.

from *Brensham Village*

May came in with sunshine as hot as June's, and Alfie sent his old ladders to be mended, for he'd need all he had at picking-time if the crop was as good as it promised to be. The fruit had set already and the petals had blown away; on every small twig you could count a score of the small green berry-like plums.

The great apple tree which stood beside the Horse Narrow was already showering its petals on the front doorstep, and its leafy branches in front of the windows made a cool green shade inside the bar. A positive choir of birds seemed to have their homes in it, so that as you drank your beer you were serenaded by a perpetual twittering and chirruping and merry fluting.

But on May the third, though the sky remained blue, there was a slight and subtle change in the weather. It was still hot enough to make you sweat if you dug in your garden or climbed the hill; but the breeze was cooler and the air felt curiously dry. We had a cricket-practice in the evening and the Colonel came down to watch us. 'What an annus mirabilis this is! It's my seventieth, and it looks like being the best fruit year I've ever known—'. He broke off abruptly, paused, and sniffed the air like a dog. Suddenly he said:

'It's going to freeze.'

'What, in May? Can you smell it?'

'I don't know if I smell it or simply feel it in my bones,' he said, 'but it's going to freeze smartish and I'm frightened for the plums.'

The Colonel always felt the weather in his bones. I never knew what he meant by this phrase, but I think it had nothing to do with the aches and pains and sharp twinges by which old people are apt to prognosticate the rain or the cold. It was something more profound than that; he meant that he was aware of coming changes as the trees in their sap feel them, as the grass at its tangled roots or the chrysalis deep in the ground feels them, as the very earth feels them, for he was nearer to these things than other men, there was something Protean about him.

When I passed through the village on my way home I glanced at the gilded weathercock on top of the church spire; and sure enough it

was beginning to swing through west to the northward, the wind had started to veer. I called on Alfie and had a look at his hygrometer. The column from the dry bulb had climbed high above the wet one showing that the air was exceptionally dry. The barometer was rising too, said Alfie. He didn't much like the look of it; but the chances of a really damaging frost so late in the season weren't very high and he said with a grin:

'If old Jack Frost takes one fruit in five, he can have 'em and welcome. They'll do with a bit of thinning. They'll burst the trees else.'

JOHN MOORE

from *The Wind in the Willows*

'Hello, Mole!' said the Water Rat.

'Hello, Rat!' said the Mole.

'Would you like to come over?' inquired the Rat presently.

'Oh, it's all very well to *talk*,' said the Mole, rather pettishly, he being new to a river and riverside life and its ways.

The Rat said nothing, but stooped and unfastened a rope and hauled on it; then lightly stepped into a little boat which the Mole had not observed. It was painted blue outside and white within, and was just the size for two animals; and the Mole's whole heart went out to it at once, even though he did not yet fully understand its uses.

The Rat sculled smartly across and made fast. Then he held up his fore-paw as the Mole stepped gingerly down. 'Lean on that!' he said. 'Now then, step lively!' and the Mole to his surprise and rapture found himself actually seated in the stern of a real boat.

'This has been a wonderful day!' said he, as the Rat shoved off and took to the sculls again. 'Do you know, I've never been in a boat before in all my life.'

'What?' cried the Rat, open-mouthed: 'Never been in a – you never – well, I – what have you been doing, then?'

'Is it so nice as all that?' asked the Mole shyly, though he was quite prepared to believe it as he leant back in his seat and surveyed the cushions, the oars, the rowlocks, and all the fascinating fittings, and felt the boat sway lightly under him.

'Nice? It's the *only* thing,' said the Water Rat solemnly, as he leant forward for his stroke. 'Believe me, my young friend, there is *nothing* – absolutely nothing – half so much worth doing as simply messing about in boats. Simply messing,' he went on dreamily: 'messing – about – in – boats; messing —'

'Look ahead, Rat!' cried the Mole suddenly.

It was too late. The boat struck the bank full tilt. The dreamer, the joyous oarsman, lay on his back at the bottom of the boat, his heels in the air.

'—about in boats – or *with* boats,' the Rat went on composedly, picking himself up with a pleasant laugh. 'In or out of 'em, it doesn't matter. Nothing seems really to matter, that's the charm of it. Whether you get away, or whether you don't; whether you arrive at your destination or whether you reach somewhere else, or whether you never get anywhere at all, you're always busy, and you never do anything in particular; and when you've done it, there's always something else to do, and you can do it if you like, but you'd much better not. Look here! If you've really nothing else on hand this morning, supposing we drop down the river together, and have a long day of it?'

The Mole waggled his toes from sheer happiness, spread his chest with a sigh of full contentment, and leaned back blissfully into the soft cushions. 'What a day I'm having!' he said. 'Let us start at once!'

'Hold hard a minute, then!' said the Rat. He looped the painter through a ring in his landing-stage, climbed up into his hole above, and after a short interval reappeared staggering under a fat, wicker luncheon-basket.

'Shove that under your feet,' he observed to the Mole, as he passed it down into the boat. Then he untied the painter and took the sculls again.

'What's inside it?' asked the Mole, wriggling with curiosity.

'There's cold chicken inside it,' replied the Rat briefly; 'cold-tonguecoldhamcoldbeefpickledgherkinssaladfrenchrollscresssand-widgespottedmeatgingerbeerlemonadesodawater—'

'O stop, stop,' cried the Mole in ecstasies: 'This is too much!'

'Do you really think so?' inquired the Rat seriously. 'It's only what I always take on these little excursions; and the other animals are always telling me that I'm a mean beast and cut it *very* fine!'

The Mole never heard a word he was saying. Absorbed in the new life he was entering upon, intoxicated with the sparkle, the ripple, the scents and the sounds and the sunlight, he trailed a paw in the water and dreamed long waking dreams. The Water Rat, like the good little fellow he was, sculled steadily on and forebore to disturb him.

KENNETH GRAHAME

The fair maid who, the first of May,
Goes to the fields at break of day
And washes in dew from the hawthorn tree,
Will ever after handsome be.

Mystery Story

A morning in May,
And we rolled up to school
In the usual way.

Well no, we didn't really,
Because the school wasn't there;
We rolled up to where
The school had been.
There was nothing.
It had all gone
And there wasn't a clue:
No hole, no scar,
Just a buttercup field
And a couple of larks
Singing over it.

You'd have thought there might be
A lot of cheering from the kids,
But there wasn't.
They all just stood around
Wondering,
Not even talking much.

ERIC FINNEY

49

JUNE

Calm weather in June,
Sets the corn in tune.

Cut your thistles before St John,
You must have two instead of one.

from *The Diary of Samuel Pepys*

7th June 1665: This morning my wife and mother rose about two
o'clock; and with Mercer, Mary, the boy, and W. Hewer, as they
had designed, took boat and down to refresh themselves on the
water to Gravesend. To the office, and meeting Creed away with
him to my Lord Treasurer's. Thence, it being the hottest day that
ever I felt in my life, we to the New Exchange and there drunk

whey, with much entreaty getting it for our money, and they would not be entreated to let us have one glasse more. So took water and to Fox-Hall, to the Spring garden, and there walked an houre or two with great pleasure, saving our minds ill at ease concerning the fleete and my Lord Sandwich, that we have no newes of them, and ill reports run up and down of his being killed, but without ground. Here staid pleasantly walking and spending but 6d. till nine at night, and then by water to White Hall, and there I stopped to hear news of the fleete, but none come, which is strange; and so by water home, where weary with walking and with the mighty heat of the weather, and for my wife's not coming home, I staying walking in the garden till twelve at night, when it begun to lighten exceedingly, through the greatness of the heat. Then despairing of her coming home, I to bed. This day, much against my will, I did in Drury Lane see two or three houses marked with a red cross upon the doors, and 'Lord have mercy upon us' writ there; which was a sad sight to me, being the first of the kind that, to my remembrance, I ever saw. It put me into an ill conception of myself and my smell, so that I was forced to buy some roll-tobacco to smell to and chaw, which took away the apprehension.

 The Swallows

All day – when early morning shone
With every dewdrop its own dawn
And when cockchafers were abroad
Hurtling like missiles that had lost their road –

The Swallows twisting here and there
Round unseen corners of the air
Upstream and down so quickly passed
I wondered that their shadows flew as fast.

They steeple-chased over the bridge
And dropped down to a drowning midge
Sharing the river with the fish,
Although the air itself was their chief dish.

Blue-winged snowballs! until they turned
And then with ruddy breasts they burned;
All in one instant everywhere,
Jugglers with their own bodies in the air.

ANDREW YOUNG

The Tale of a Tail

It was eleven o'clock at night on Midsummer Eve. A fine large moon was sailing high in the sky and Mrs Spriggins' garden looked all silvery in the moonlight.

There was a warm spicy smell from the deep red Clove pinks that grew under the kitchen window. But she was not thinking of Clove pinks. She was vexed and worried and every few minutes she said to herself, 'Dear, dear, dearie me – wherever can he be?' And she shook her head and looked across the meadow where a big fairy-ring showed quite plain in the moonlight.

'If the Good Folk catch him up to his tricks on Midsummer Eve, he'll get into trouble, so he will,' said Mrs Spriggins. And she leaned out of the window and called very loud, 'Kitty, kitty, kitty! Mr Wickens, Mr Wickens, kitty, kitty-cat!'

'Mr Wickens', as perhaps you have guessed, was the name of Mrs Spriggins' cat. It is an odd name for a cat, but it seemed to suit him very well indeed. He was large and dignified, with a wise, kind face and a satin-smooth dark tabby coat.

Mr Wickens wore a little leather collar round his neck, like a dog. Fastened to the collar was a tiny tinkling bell; that was to keep him from catching birds. However quietly he crept, the bell tinkled as he moved and the birds heard it and flew away before he reached them.

But on moonlight nights in summer-time Mr Wickens liked to take a walk in the fields, and several times, in spite of his tinkling bell, he had brought back a baby rabbit in his mouth. He carried it quite gently, as a mother-cat carries a kitten, and it was not hurt though it was very frightened. He always trotted in, looking very proud and pleased, and laid the rabbit down in Mrs Spriggins' kitchen and mewed and purred till Mrs Spriggins came to see what he had brought. She could never make him understand that baby rabbits were no use at all to her. Each time, she had to make a nest in a basket and feed the rabbit till it was old enough to scamper away.

So Mrs Spriggins sat by her kitchen window waiting, and hoping there would not be a baby rabbit that night, because she wanted to go to bed. She got up from her chair to look at the time and the hands of the tall grandfather clock were almost together. It was very nearly twelve o'clock. But as she leaned out of the window again she heard a little far-off tinkling sound in the stillness, and she said to herself, 'There he is!'

She could see a little black shadow on the far side of the meadow, slipping along in the moonlight. It was Mr Wickens.

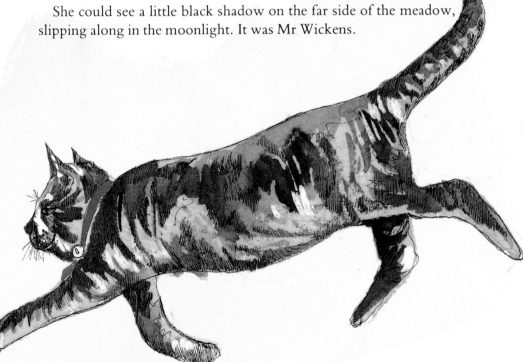

'Oh dear,' said Mrs Spriggins, 'he's brought me another.' She could see a little bundle in his mouth. 'Be quick,' she called, 'you naughty cat. It's nearly twelve o'clock.' Just as she spoke the big church clock began to strike, and Mr Wickens reached the edge of the fairy-ring.

He gave a jump because the grass grew tall and thick round the ring; and as he jumped – he was gone. There was the fairy-ring, like a ring of shadow rather ragged at the edges. But where were Mr Wickens and his baby rabbit? They were nowhere at all!

Mrs Spriggins got up from her chair and ran down the garden path, and along the little trodden path that led through the meadow beyond.

She left the path and hurried across to the fairy-ring and stood looking at it. There it was, all quiet and empty; there was not a sound of a tinkling bell, not a shadow, not a purr, not a mew.

'The Good Folk have taken away my Kitty Wickens,' she said to herself.

She was so upset that she was almost crying, and then something touched her face and tickled her nose and made her sneeze instead. It was something velvety and soft as silk. Mrs Spriggins rubbed her nose and looked to see what it could be. Waving in the moonlight, quite close to her and just outside the fairy-ring, was the tip of Mr Wickens' long smooth tail – only the tip, there was no more of the tail. It ended where the fairy-ring began.

Then she knew what had happened. She had heard her grandmother say that once you stepped inside a fairy-ring on a Midsummer moonlight night, the Good Folk had power over you. If they chose, no one could see or hear you. They charmed your feet, and they charmed your eyes and your ears.

'But they forgot to charm my Kitty Wickens' tail,' said Mrs Spriggins. 'And I'll get him out again, that I will.'

She went to bed, but she did not sleep much, as you may guess. She woke very early, while the birds were still whispering to one another, and she lay thinking. Presently she said to herself, 'I'll ask Mrs Featherstone to help me.'

Mrs Featherstone thought Mr Wickens was a dear good cat – as indeed he was – so she was quite ready to help. She came along to Mrs Spriggins' cottage at sunset; and as the moon came up, Mrs Spriggins and Mrs Featherstone came down the garden path. They each carried a little three-legged wooden stool and they had brought their knitting with them to pass the time away.

So there they sat, on their wooden stools at the edge of the fairy-ring, as the moon came creeping up the sky like a golden ball of light.

Eleven o'clock passed and there was no sign of Mr Wickens or his tail. Twelve o'clock began to strike from the church tower, and as it struck Mrs Spriggins suddenly shouted 'There it is!'

She dropped her knitting and leaned forward and snatched at something that floated in the air just in front of her. It was the tip of Mr Wickens' tail! She held it fast and she could feel him dig in his toes and pull gently against her. And then – as she leaned forward, the three-legged stool tilted and Mrs Spriggins fell, right into the fairy-ring. And what would have been the end of this story if Mrs Featherstone had not been there, I really cannot tell.

There was Mrs Spriggins inside the fairy-ring. She had tight hold of Mr Wickens, it is true; and she could feel him as she fell, and she grabbed him with one hand and held him fast. But he seemed as heavy as lead, and her hands and her knees and her toes felt full of pins and needles and would not move; and thousands of tiny shining, sparkling wings were dancing before her eyes.

Mrs Spriggins blinked and shut her eyes because they dazzled so, but she held firm and she could feel that Mr Wickens was purring, so she was sure there was nothing to be really afraid of. Then she felt a tug and she knew what was happening. Mrs Featherstone had caught her by the arm as she fell and she was pulling her out of the fairy-ring. Mrs Featherstone could see nothing of Mrs Spriggins except her hand, but she held that and pulled and tugged with all her might. And all in a moment – just like a fish out of a pool – out came Mrs Spriggins into the moonlight and out came Mr Wickens too.

And Mrs Featherstone said, 'Well!' She had no breath to say anything more. And Mrs Spriggins said, 'Well!' She had no breath either. Then they picked up their three-legged stools and carried them to the path, quite away from the edge of the fairy-ring.

Mrs Spriggins said, 'Thank you, Mrs Featherstone, my dear.'

Mrs Featherstone said, 'Mrs Spriggins, my dear, I'm sure you're very welcome.'

Then they picked up their three-legged stools and walked across the field and up the garden path to Mrs Spriggins' door. And they each had a large bowl of bread-and-milk, and Mr Wickens – who was very hungry, poor cat – had one too.

It was one o'clock in the morning by the time they had finished their bread-and milk and their talk about the very queer things that had happened. They said 'good-night' at last, and Mrs Spriggins lit the lantern for Mrs Featherstone because the moon was setting and it was really very dark under the trees.

She stood at her cottage door and watched Mrs Featherstone and the lantern go bobbing away down the garden path. Then she shut the door and stroked Mr Wickens, feeling very glad she had him there safe and sound to stroke. Mr Wickens nudged her with his nose, which was his way of stroking, and he jumped into the cushioned arm-chair and curled himself up to sleep and Mrs Spriggins climbed the stairs to bed.

What became of the baby rabbit that Mr Wickens carried with him into the fairy-ring, I do not know. But no doubt the Good Folk cared for it and sent it back to its mother. As Mr Wickens never brought another to Mrs Spriggins, they must certainly have explained to him that no really kind cat would steal a baby rabbit. And being a really kind cat, Mr Wickens stole no more. And I expect that pleases you almost as much as it pleased Mrs Spriggins.

ELIZABETH CLARK

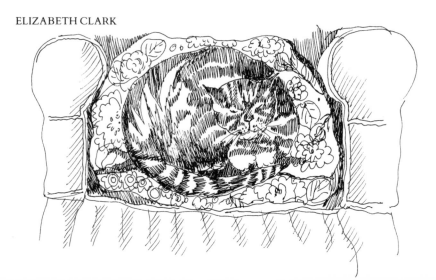

The Song of the Scarlet Pimpernel Fairy

By the furrowed field I lie,
Calling to the passers-by:
'If the weather you would tell,
Look at Scarlet Pimpernel.'

When the day is warm and fine,
I unfold these flowers of mine;
Ah, but you must look for rain
When I shut them up again!

Weather-glasses on the walls
Hang in wealthy people's halls:
Though I lie where cart-wheels pass,
I'm the Poor Man's Weather-Glass!

CICELY M BARKER

JULY

St Swithin's Day if thou dost rain
For forty days it will remain.

The Balloon Man

He always comes on market days,
    And holds balloons – a lovely bunch –
And in the market square he stays,
    And never seems to think of lunch.

They're red and purple, blue and green,
    And when it is a sunny day
Tho' carts and people get between
    You see them shining far away.

And some are big and some are small,
    All tied together with a string,
And if there is a wind at all
    They tug and tug like anything.

Some day perhaps he'll let them go
    And we shall see them sailing high,
And stand and watch them from below –
    They would look pretty in the sky!

ROSE FYLEMAN

Why the Dog's Nose is Always Cold

What makes the dog's nose always cold?
I'll try to tell you, curls of gold.
Well, years and years, and years ago –
How many I don't really know –
There came a rain on sea and shore;
Its like was never seen before
Or since. It fell unceasing down,
Till all the world began to drown;
But just before the rain did pour,
An old, old man – his name was Noah –
Built an ark, that he might save
His family from a watery grave,
And in it also he designed
To shelter two of every kind
Of beast. Well dear, when it was done,
And heavy clouds obscured the sun,
The Noah folks to it quickly ran,
And then the animals began
Gravely to march along in pairs,
The leopards, tigers, wolves and bears,
The deer, the hippopotamuses,
The rabbits, squirrels, elks, walruses,
The camels, goats, and cats and donkeys,
The tall giraffes, the beavers, monkeys,
The rats, the big rhinoceroses,
The dromedaries and the horses,
The sheep, the mice, the kangeroos,
Hyenas, elephants, koo-doos,
And hundreds more – 'twould take all day,
My dear, so many names to say –

And at the very, very end
Of the procession, by his friend
And master, faithful dog was seen,
The livelong time he'd helping been
To drive the crowd of creatures in,
And now, with loud exultant bark,
He gaily sprang aboard the ark.
Alas! so crowded was the space
He could not in it find a place,
So patiently he turned about –
Stood half-way in and half-way out.

And those extremely heavy showers
Descended through nine hundred hours
And more; and, darling, at their close,
'Most frozen was his honest nose,
And never could it lose again
The dampness of that dreadful rain;
And that is what, my curls of gold,
Makes all the doggies' noses cold.

MARGARET EYTINGE

The Lighthouse

What I remember best about
my holiday was how, each night,
the lighthouse kept sweeping my bedroom
with its clean, cool ray of light.

I lay there, tucked up in the blankets,
and suddenly the lighthouse shone:
a switched on torch that stabbed the night
like a murderer and moved on.

Then back it came, out of the dark,
and swung round, as in some fixed plan:
the light of the lighthouse – opening,
folding, and closing like a fan.

RAYMOND WILSON

School Buses

You'd think that by the end of June they'd take them-
  selves
Away, get out of sight – but no, they don't; they
Don't at all. You see them waiting through
July in clumps of sumac near the railroad, or
Behind a service station, watching, always watching
  for a
Child who's let go of summer's hand and strayed. I
  have
Seen them hunting on the roads of August – empty
  buses
Scanning woods and ponds with rows of empty eyes.
  This morning
I saw five of them, parked like a week of
Schooldays, smiling slow in orange paint and
Smirking with their mirrors in the sun –
But summer isn't done! Not yet!

RUSSELL HOBAN

The Ice

Her day out from the workhouse-ward, she stands,
A grey-haired woman decent and precise,
With brim black bonnet and neat paisley shawl,
Among the other children by the stall,
And with grave relish eats a penny ice.

To wizened toothless gums with quaking hands
She holds it, shuddering with delicious cold,
Nor heeds the jeering laughter of young men –
The happiest, in her innocence, of all:
For, while their insolent youth must soon grow old,
She, who's been old, is now a child again.

WILFRID GIBSON

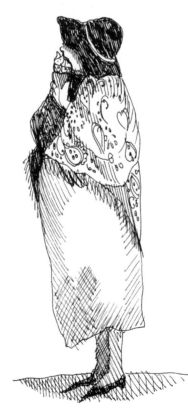

Holidays at Home

There was a family who, every year,
Would go abroad, sometimes to Italy,
Sometimes to France. The youngest did not dare
To say, 'I much prefer to stay right here.'

You see, abroad there were no slot-machines,
No bright pink rock with one name going through it,
No rain, no boarding-houses, no baked beans,
No landladies, and no familiar scenes.

And George, the youngest boy, so longed to say,
'I don't like Greece. I don't like all these views,
I don't like having fierce sun every day,
And, most of all, I just detest the way

The food is cooked – that garlic and that soup,
Those strings of pasta, and no cakes at all.'
The family wondered why George seemed to droop
And looked just like a thin hen in a coop.

They never guessed why when they said, 'Next year
We can't afford abroad, we'll stay right here,'
George looked so pleased and soon began to dream
Of piers, pink rock, deep sand, and Devonshire cream.

ELIZABETH JENNINGS

AUGUST

After Lammas★ corn ripens as much by night as by day.

★ Lammas Day is August 1st.

High Summer on the Mountains

High summer on the mountains
And on the clover leas,
And on the local sidings,
And on the rhubarb leaves.

Brass bands in all the valleys
Blaring defiant tunes,
Crowds, acclaiming carnival,
Prize pigs and wooden spoons

Dust on shabby hedgerows
Behind the colliery wall,
Dust on rail and girder
And tram and prop and all.

High summer on the slag heaps
And on polluted streams,
And old men in the morning
Telling the town their dreams.

IDRIS DAVIES

Blackberry Picking

Late August, given heavy rain and sun
For a full week, the blackberries would ripen.
At first, just one, a glossy purple clot
Among others, red, green, hard as a knot.
You ate that first one and its flesh was sweet
Like thickened wine: summer's blood was in it
Leaving stains upon the tongue and lust for
Picking. Then red ones inked up and that hunger
Sent us out with milk-cans, pea-tins, jam-pots
Where briars scratched and wet grass bleached our boots.
Round hayfields, cornfields and potato-drills
We trekked and picked until the cans were full,
Until the tinkling bottom had been covered
With green ones, and on top big dark blobs burned
Like a plate of eyes. Our hands were peppered
With thorn pricks, our palms sticky as Bluebeard's.

We hoarded the fresh berries in the byre.
But when the bath was filled we found a fur,
A rat-grey fungus, glutting on our cache.
The juice was stinking too. Once off the bush
The fruit fermented, the sweet flesh would turn sour.
I always felt like crying. It wasn't fair
That all the lovely canfuls smelt of rot.
Each year I hoped they'd keep, knew they would not.

SEAMUS HEANEY

72

from *Cider with Rosie*

Summer was also the time of these: of sudden plenty, of slow hours and actions, of diamond haze and dust on the eyes, of the valley in post-vernal slumber; of burying birds out of seething corruption; of Mother sleeping heavily at noon; of jazzing wasps and dragonflies, haystooks and thistle-seeds, snows of white butteflies, skylarks' eggs, bee-orchids, and frantic ants; of wolf-cub parades, and boy scouts' bugles; of sweat running down the legs; of boiling potatoes on bramble fires, of flames glass-blue in the sun; of lying naked in the hill-cold stream; begging pennies for bottles of pop; of girls' bare arms and unripe cherries, green apples and liquid walnuts; of fires and falls and new-scabbed knees, sobbing pursuits and flights; of picnics high up in the crumbling quarries, of butter running like oil, of sunstroke, fever, and cucumber peel stuck cool to one's burning brow. All this, and the feeling that it would never end, that such days had come for ever, with the pump drying up and the water-butt crawling, and the chalk ground hard as the moon. All sights twice-brilliant and smells twice-sharp, all game-days twice as long. Double charged as we were, like the meadow ants, with the frenzy of the sun, we used up the light to its last violet drop, and even then couldn't go to bed.

When darkness fell, and the huge moon rose, we stirred to a second life. Then boys went calling along the roads, wild slit-eyed animal calls, Walt Kerry's naked nasal yodel, Boney's jackal scream. As soon as we heard them we crept outdoors, out of our stifling bedrooms, stepped out into moonlight warm as the sun to join our chalk-white, moon-masked gang.

Games in the moon. Games of pursuit and capture. Games that the night demanded. Best of all, Fox and Hounds – go where you like, and the whole of the valley to hunt through. Two chosen boys loped away through the trees and were immediately swallowed in shadow. We gave them five minutes, then set off after them. They had churchyard, farmyard, barns, quarries, hilltops, and woods to run to. They had all night, and the whole of the moon, and five miles of country to hide in . . .

Padding softly, we ran under the melting stars, through sharp garlic woods, through blue blazed fields, following the scent by the game's one rule, the question and answer cry. Every so often, panting for breath, we paused to check on our quarry. Bullet heads lifted, teeth shone in the moon. 'Whistle-or-'OLLER! Or-we-shall-not-FOLLER!' It was a cry on two notes, prolonged. From the other side of the hill, above white fields of mist, the faint fox-cry came back. We were off again then, through the waking night, among sleepless owls and badgers, while our quarry slipped off into another parish and would not be found for hours.

Round about midnight we ran them to earth, exhausted under a haystack. Until then we had chased them through all the world, through jungles, swamps, and tundras, across pampas plains and steppes of wheat and plateaux of shooting stars, while hares made love in the silver grasses, and the large hot moon climbed over us, raising tides in my head of night and summer that move there even yet.

LAURIE LEE

from *The Prelude*

One evening (surely I was led by her)
I went alone into a shepherd's boat,
A skiff that to a willow tree was tied
Within a rocky cave, its usual home.
'Twas by the shores of Patterdale, a vale
Wherein I was a stranger, thither come
A schoolboy traveller, at the holidays.
Forth rambled from the village inn alone
No sooner had I sight of this small skiff,
Discover'd thus by unexpected chance,
Than I unloos'd her tether and embark'd.
The moon was up, the lake was shining clear
Among the hoary mountains; from the shore
I push'd, and struck the oars and struck again
In cadence, and my little boat mov'd on
Even like a Man who walks with stately step
Though bent on speed. It was an act of stealth
And troubled pleasure; not without the voice
Of mountain-echoes did my boat move on;
Leaving behind her still, on either side,
Small circles glittering idly in the moon,
Until they melted all into one track
Of sparkling light. A rocky steep uprose
Above the cavern of the willow tree
And now, as suited one who proudly row'd
With his best skill, I fix'd a steady view
Upon the top of that same craggy ridge,
The bound of the horizon, for behind
Was nothing but the stars and the grey sky.
She was an elfin pinnace; lustily
I dipp'd my oars into the silent lake,
And, as I rose upon the stroke, my boat

Went heaving through the water like a swan;
When from behind that craggy steep till then
The bound of the horizon, a huge cliff,
As if with voluntary power instinct,
Uprear'd its head. I struck and struck again,
And growing still in stature the huge cliff
Rose up between me and the stars, and still,
With measur'd motion, like a living thing,
Strode after me. With trembling hands I turn'd,
And through the silent water stole my way
Back to the cavern of the willow tree;
There in her mooring-place I left my bark,
And through the meadows homeward went, with grave
And serious thoughts, and after I had seen
That spectacle, for many days, my brain
Work'd with a dim and undetermin'd sense
Of unknown modes of being; in my thoughts
There was a darkness, call it solitude
Or blank desertion. No familiar shapes
Of hourly objects, images of trees,
Of sea or sky, no colours of green fields;
But huge and mighty forms, that do not live
Like living men, mov'd slowly through my mind
By day, and were the trouble of my dreams.

WILLIAM WORDSWORTH

SEPTEMBER

So many days old the moon is on Michaelmas Day,★
So many floods after.

★September 29th

Fox

Who
Wears the smartest evening dress in England?
Checks his watch by the stars
And hurries, white-scarfed,
To the opera
In the flea-ridden hen-house
Where he will conduct the orchestra?

Who
With a Robin Hood mask over his eyes
Meets King Pheasant the Magnificent
And with silent laughter
Shakes all the gold out of his robes
Then carries him bodily home
Over his shoulder,
A swag-bag?

And who
Flinging back his Dracula cloak
And letting one fang wink in the moonlight
Lifts off his top hat
Shows us the moon through the bottom of it
Then brings out of it, in a flourish of feathers,
The gander we locked up at sunset?

TED HUGHES

Nerves [2 September 1939]

I think I'll get a paper,
I think I'd better wait.
I'll hear the news at six o'clock,
That's much more up to date.

It's just like last September,
Absurd how time stands still;
They're bound to make a statement.
I don't suppose they will.

I think I'd better stroll around.
Perhaps it's best to stay.
I think I'll have a whisky neat,
I can't this time of day.

I think I'll have another smoke.
I don't know what to do.
I promised to ring someone up,
I can't remember who.

They say it's been averted.
They say we're on the brink.
I'll wait for the *New Statesman*,
I wonder what they think.

They're shouting. It's a Special.
It's not. It's just street cries.
I think the heat is frightful.
God damn those bloody flies.

I see the nation's keeping cool,
The public calm is fine.
This crisis can't shake England's nerves.
It's playing hell with mine.

'SAGITTARIUS' (OLGA KATZIN)

Harvest Hymn

We plough the fields and scatter
our pesticides again:
our seeds are fed and watered
by gentle acid rain.
We spray the corn in winter
till pests and weeds are dead –
who minds a little poison
inside his daily bread?

All good gifts around us
beneath our ozone layer
are safe, oh Lord,
so thank you Lord
that we know how to care.

JUDITH NICHOLLS

A Day in Autumn

It will not always be like this,
The air windless, a few last
Leaves adding their decoration
To the trees' shoulders, braiding the cuffs
Of the boughs with gold; a bird preening
In the lawn's mirror. Having looked up
From the day's chores, pause a minute,
Let the mind take its photograph
Of the bright scene, something to wear
Against the heart in the long cold.

R S THOMAS

September blow soft
Until apples are in loft.

Conkers

Out of sight they spend whole summers
growing spiky in the leaf corners.
We never hear them drop:
their swell and fall
is secret as imagination.
In split shells they lie,

nuggets for polishing.
Damp from casings briefly clings
like mist across the sunrise.
They burnish in our hands,
send bubbles through the blood,
make minds molten with joy.

They are poems, varied
and irresistible,
each containing
its own new germination.
Arranging them on strings
will thread our Autumn through with fire.

BARRIE WADE

from *The Creeping Man*

It was one Sunday evening early in September of the year 1903 that I received one of Holmes' laconic messages: 'Come at once if convenient – if inconvenient come all the same. S.H.' The relations between us in those latter days were peculiar. He was a man of habits, narrow and concentrated habits, and I had become one of them. As an institution I was like the violin, the shag tobacco, the old black pipe, the index books, and others perhaps less excusable. When it was a case of active work and a comrade was needed upon whose nerve he could place some reliance, my role was obvious. But apart from this I had uses. I was a whetstone for his mind. I stimulated him. He liked to think aloud in my presence. His remarks could hardly be said to be made to me – many of them would have been as appropriately addressed to his bedstead – but none the less, having formed the habit it had become in some way helpful that I should register and interject. If I irritated him by a certain methodical slowness in my mentality, that irritation served only to make his own flame-like intuitions and impressions flash up the more vividly and swiftly. Such was my humble role in our alliance.

When I arrived at Baker Street I found him huddled up in his armchair with updrawn knees, his pipe in his mouth and his brow furrowed with thought. It was clear that he was in the throes of some vexatious problem. With a wave of his hand he indicated my old armchair, but otherwise for half an hour he gave no sign that he was aware of my presence. Then with a start he seemed to come from his reverie, and, with his usual whimsical smile, he greeted me back to what had once been my home.

'You will excuse a certain abstraction of mind, my dear Watson,' said he. 'Some curious facts have been submitted to me within the last twenty-four hours, and they in turn have given rise to some speculations of a more general character. I have serious thoughts of writing a small monograph upon the use of dogs in the work of the detective.'

'But surely, Holmes, this has been explored,' said I. 'Bloodhounds – sleuth-hounds—'

'No, no, Watson; that side of the matter is, of course, obvious. But there is another which is far more subtle. You may recollect that in the case which you, in your sensational way, coupled with the Copper Beeches, I was able, by watching the mind of the child, to form a deduction as to the criminal habits of the very smug and respectable father.'

'Yes, I remember it well.'

'My line of thoughts about dogs is analogous. A dog reflects the family life. Whoever saw a frisky dog in a gloomy family, or a sad dog in a happy one? Snarling people have snarling dogs, dangerous people have dangerous ones. And their passing moods may reflect the passing moods of others.'

I shook my head. 'Surely, Holmes, this is a little far-fetched,' said I.

He had refilled his pipe and resumed his seat, taking no notice of my comment.

'The practical application of what I have said is very close to the problem which I am investigating. It is a tangled skein, you understand, and I am looking for a loose end. One possible loose end lies in the question: Why does Professor Presbury's faithful wolf-hound, Roy, endeavour to bite him?'

SIR ARTHUR CONAN DOYLE

OCTOBER

A good October and a good blast
To blow the hogs acorns and mast.

from *Henry V*

This day is called the Feast of Crispian.
He that outlives this day, and comes safe home,
Will stand a-tiptoe when this day is named,
And rouse him at the name of Crispian.
He that shall live this day, and see old age,
Will yearly on the vigil feast his neighbours
And say, 'To-morrow is Saint Crispian.'
Then will he strip his sleeve and show his scars,
And say, 'These wounds I had on Crispin's day.'
Old men forget; yet all shall be forgot,
But he'll remember, with advantages,
What feats he did that day. Then shall our names,
Familiar in his mouth as household words –
Harry the King, Bedford and Exeter,
Warwick and Talbot, Salisbury and Gloucester –
Be in their flowing cups freshly rememb'red.
This story shall the good man teach his son;
And Crispin Crispian shall ne'er go by,
From this day to the ending of the world,
But we in it shall be remembered –
We few, we happy few, we band of brothers;
For he to-day that sheds his blood with me
Shall be my brother. Be he ne'er so vile,
This day shall gentle his condition;
And gentlemen in England now a-bed
Shall think themselves accursed they were not here,
And hold their manhoods cheap whiles any speaks
That fought with us upon Saint Crispin's day.

WILLIAM SHAKESPEARE

87

from *Black Beauty*

One day late in the autumn, my master had a long journey to go on business. I was put into the dog-cart, and John went with his master. I always liked to go in the dog-cart, it was so light, and the high wheels ran along so pleasantly. There had been a great deal of rain, and now the wind was very high, and blew the dry leaves across the road in a shower. We went along merrily till we came to the toll-bar, and the low wooden bridge.

The man at the gate said the river was rising fast, and he feared it would be a bad night.

When we got to the town, of course, I had a good wait, but as the master's business engaged him a long time, we did not start for home till rather late in the afternoon. The wind was then much higher, and I heard the master say to John, he had never been out in such a storm; and so I thought, as we went along the skirts of a wood, where the great branches were swaying about like twigs, and the rushing sound was terrible.

'I wish we were well out of this wood,' said my master.

'Yes, sir,' said John, 'it would be rather awkward if one of these branches came down upon us.'

The words were scarcely out of his mouth, when there was a groan, and a crack, and a splitting sound, and tearing crashing down amongst the other trees came an oak, torn up by the roots, and it fell right across the road just before us. John jumped out and was in a moment at my head.

'That was a very near touch,' said my master. 'What's to be done now?'

'Well, sir, we can't drive over that tree nor yet round it; there will
be nothing for it but to go back to the four crossways, and that will
be a good six miles before we get round to the wooden bridge again;
it will make us late, but the horse is fresh.'

So back we went, and round by the crossroads; but by the time we
got to the bridge it was very nearly dark, we could just see that the
water was over the middle of it; but as that happened sometimes
when the floods were out, master did not stop. We were going along
at a good pace, but the moment my feet touched the first part of the
bridge, I felt sure there was something wrong. I dare not go forward,
and I made a dead stop. 'Go on, Beauty,' said my master, and he
gave me a touch with the whip, but I dare not stir; he gave me a
sharp cut, I jumped, but I dare not go forward.

'There's something wrong, sir,' said John, and he sprang out of
the dog-cart and came to my head and looked all about. He tried to
lead me forward, 'Come on, Beauty, what's the matter?' Of course I
could not tell him, but I knew very well that the bridge was not safe.

Just then the man at the toll-gate on the other side ran out of the
house, tossing a torch about like one mad.

'Hoy, hoy, hoy, halloo, stop!' he cried.

'What's the matter?' shouted my master.

'The bridge is broken in the middle and part of it is carried away; if
you come on you'll be into the river.'

'Thank God!' said my master. 'You Beauty!' said John and took the bridle and gently turned me round to the right-hand road by the river side. The sun had set some time, the wind seemed to have lulled off after that furious blast which tore up the tree. It grew darker and darker, stiller and stiller. For a good while neither master nor John spoke, and then master began in a serious voice. I could not understand much of what they said, but I found they thought, if I had gone on as the master wanted me, most likely the bridge would have given way under us, and horse, chaise, master, and man would have fallen into the river; and as the current was flowing very strongly, and there was no light and no help at hand, it was more than likely we should all have been drowned.

At last we came to the Park gates, and found the gardener looking out for us. He said that mistress had been in a dreadful way ever since dark, fearing some accident had happened.

We saw a light at the hall door and at the upper windows, and as we came up mistress ran out, saying, 'Are you really safe, my dear? Oh! I have been so anxious, fancying all sorts of things. Have you had no accident?'

'No, my dear; but if your Black Beauty had not been wiser than we were, we should all have been carried down the river at the wooden bridge.' I heard no more, as they went into the house, and John took me to the stable. Oh! what a good supper he gave me that night, a good bran mash and some crushed beans with my oats, and such a thick bed of straw, and I was glad of it, for I was tired.

ANNA SEWELL

The Alchemist

The sheet of writing paper
Slowly became a leaf of gold,
Changing under my hand.
I looked up,
And close about the window
Saw soft mallets of fog
Thudding upon the sun;
Saw him cool from fire to bronze,
To aluminium,
To water,
And vanish.

RICHARD CHURCH

Biddy and the Hallowe'en Cat

It was the night of Hallowe'en. Everyone in the village was in bed and asleep, except old Biddy. She still sat at her spinning wheel.

Scritch-scratch! There was a sound at the door.

'Who's there?' asked Old Biddy, but there was no answer. Old Biddy went on spinning.

Scritch-scratch! 'Let me in! Let me in!' cried a voice.

'Faith, I'll do no such thing at this hour of night!' said Biddy and she went on spinning.

Scritch-scratch! 'Let me in! It's cold and hungry I am,' cried the voice again.

'Sure, it must be a lost child,' thought old Biddy. 'What harm to let it in!' and she opened the door.

And in came a black cat and three black kittens, each with its tail up in the air like a poker. The cats walked across the room and sat themselves down close to the warm peat fire and began to purr.

''Pon me word!' said old Biddy and went on spinning.

'Biddy dear,' said the black cat, 'would there be any milk in the house? We're desperate hungry.'

Biddy stopped her spinning wheel, fetched a bowl and filled it with milk from the brown crock. The four cats shut their eyes and lapped until the bowl was clean. Biddy went on spinning.

'Thank you, Biddy dear,' said the black cat. 'What ails you that you're not in bed on such a night?'

'Leave me be!' said Biddy crossly. 'I'll go to me bed when I please.'

The black cat jumped on to the creepie stool at Biddy's side. 'Biddy dear,' it said. 'Will you listen now! The Little People are waitin' to hold their Hallowe'en feast and dance in your kitchen. It's mortal angry they are to be kept out in the cold. Be off with you to your bed, woman!'

Whoosh! The black cat sprang up the chimney with her three kittens after her. Just as the tail of the last one disappeared, there was a chinking sound on the hearth.

The old woman ran to see what it was. There lay a shining silver coin worth more than she could earn in a month!

Biddy lost no time but went straight to bed. Even before she could lay her head down on the pillow, she could hear the sound of fairy music and the tap of dancing feet.

Never again did old Biddy stay up late on Hallowe'en night.

TRADITIONAL

NOVEMBER

Where the wind is on Martinmas Eve*, there it will be
the rest of the winter.

*November 11th

Daffodils

Bulbs planted, their long, cool sleep begins,
Laid away in the dark, three bowls,
Life locked–up, sunlight hidden in tight folds.
Two months, for winter's green blades
To pierce the chill air, welcome a new year.
Some morning of surprise a dozen trumpets will sound
The dark's ending with a gold salute.
The world will shine then, three bowls
Make the house beautiful with a little spring,
My eyes full of flowers.

LEONARD CLARK

Elegy for J.F.K. (November 22nd 1963)

Why *then*, why *there*,
Why *thus*, we cry, did he die?
The heavens are silent.

What he was, he was:
What he is fated to become
Depends on us.

Remembering his death,
How we choose to live
Will decide its meaning.

When a just man dies,
Lamentation and praise,
Sorrow and joy, are one.

W H AUDEN

Gunpowder Plot

For days these curious cardboard buds have lain
In brightly coloured boxes. Soon the night
Will come. We pray there'll be no sullen rain
To make these magic orchids flame less bright.

Now in the garden's darkness they begin
To flower: the frenzied whizz of Catherine-wheel
Puts forth its fiery petals and the thin
Rocket soars to burst upon the steel

Bulwark of a cloud. And then the guy,
Absurdly human phoenix, is again
Gulped by greedy flames: the harvest sky
Is flecked with threshed and glittering golden grain.

'Uncle! A cannon! Watch me as I light it!'
The women helter-skelter, squealing high,
Retreat; the paper fuse is quickly lit,
A cat-like hiss, and spit of fire, a sly

Falter, then the air is shocked with blast.
The cannon bangs and in my nostrils drifts
A bitter scent that brings the lurking past
Lurching to my side. The present shifts,

Allows a ten-year memory to walk
Unhindered now; and so I'm forced to hear
The banshee howl of mortar and the talk
Of men who died, am forced to taste my fear.

I listen for a moment to the guns,
The torn earth's grunts, recalling how I prayed.
The past retreats. I hear a corpse's sons –
'Who's scared of bangers!' 'Uncle! John's afraid!'

VERNON SCANNELL

97

For the Fallen (1914)

With proud thanksgiving, a mother for her children,
England mourns for her dead across the sea.
Flesh of her flesh they were, spirit of her spirit,
Fallen in the cause of the free.

Solemn the drums thrill: Death august and royal
Sings sorrow up into immortal spheres.
There is music in the midst of desolation
And a glory that shines upon our tears.

They went with songs to the battle, they were young,
Straight of limb, true of eye, steady and aglow.
They were staunch to the end against odds uncounted,
They fell with their faces to the foe.

They shall grow not old, as we that are left grow old:
Age shall not weary them, nor the years condemn.
At the going down of the sun and in the morning
We will remember them.

They mingle not with their laughing comrades again:
They sit no more at familiar tables of home;
They have no lot in our labour of the day-time;
They sleep beyond England's foam.

But where our desires are and our hopes profound,
Felt as a well-spring that is hidden from sight,
To the innermost heart of their own land they are known
As the stars are known to the Night;

As the stars that shall be bright when we are dust,
Moving in marches upon the heavenly plain,
As the stars that are starry in the time of our darkness,
To the end, to the end, they remain.

LAURENCE BINYON

from *Bleak House*

London. Michaelmas Term lately over, and the Lord Chancellor sitting in Lincoln's Inn Hall. Implacable November weather. As much mud in the streets as if the waters had but newly retired from the face of the earth, and it would not be wonderful to meet a Megalosaurus, forty feet long or so, waddling like an elephantine lizard up Holborn Hill. Smoke lowering down from chimney-pots, making a soft black drizzle, with flakes of soot in it as big as full-grown snowflakes – gone into mourning, one might imagine, for the death of the sun. Dogs, undistinguishable in mire. Horses, scarcely better; splashed to their very blinkers. Foot passengers, jostling one another's umbrellas, in a general infection of ill-temper, and losing their foothold at street-corners, where tens of thousands of other foot passengers have been slipping and sliding since the day broke (if this day ever broke), adding new deposits to the crust upon crust of mud, sticking at those points tenaciously to the pavement, and accumulating at compound interest.

Fog everywhere. Fog up the river, where it flows among green aits and meadows; fog down the river, where it rolls defiled among the tiers of shipping, and the waterside pollutions of a great (and dirty) city. Fog on the Essex marshes, fog on the Kentish heights. Fog creeping into the cabooses of collier-brigs, fog lying out on the yards, and hovering in the rigging of great ships; fog drooping on the gunwales of barges and small boats. Fog in the eyes and throats of ancient Greenwich pensioners, wheezing by the firesides of their wards; fog in the stem and bowl of the afternoon pipe of the wrathful skipper, down in his close cabin; fog cruelly pinching the toes and fingers of his shivering little 'prentice boy on deck. Chance people on the bridges peeping over the parapets into a nether sky of fog, with fog all round them, as if they were up in a balloon, and hanging in the misty clouds.

Gas looming through the fog in divers places in the streets, much as the sun may, from the spongy fields, be seen to loom by husband-man and ploughboy. Most of the shops lighted two hours before their time – as the gas seems to know, for it has a haggard and unwilling look.

The raw afternoon is rawest, and the dense fog is densest, and the muddy streets are muddiest, near that leaden-headed old obstruction, appropriate ornament for the threshold of a leaden-headed old corporation: Temple Bar. And hard by Temple Bar, in Lincoln's Inn Hall, at the very heart of the fog, sits the Lord High Chancellor in his High Court of Chancery.

CHARLES DICKENS

Ancient Music

Winter is icummen in,
Lhude sing Goddamm,
Raineth drop and staineth slop,
And how the wind doth ramm!
    Sing: Goddamm.
Skiddeth bus and sloppeth us,
An ague hath my ham.
Freezeth river, turneth liver,
    Damn you, sing: Goddamm.
Goddamm, Goddamm, 'tis why I am, Goddamm,
    So 'gainst the winter's balm.
Sing goddamm, dam, sing Goddamm,
Sing goddamm, sing goddamm, DAMM.

EZRA POUND

DECEMBER

St Thomas gray! St Thomas gray! the longest night and the shortest day.★

★St Thomas's Day is December 21st.

A Season

First snow
   falling,
Wild geese
   calling.
Fields
   bare,
Winter
   whispers
     everywhere

LILLIAN M FISHER

Snow and Ice Poems

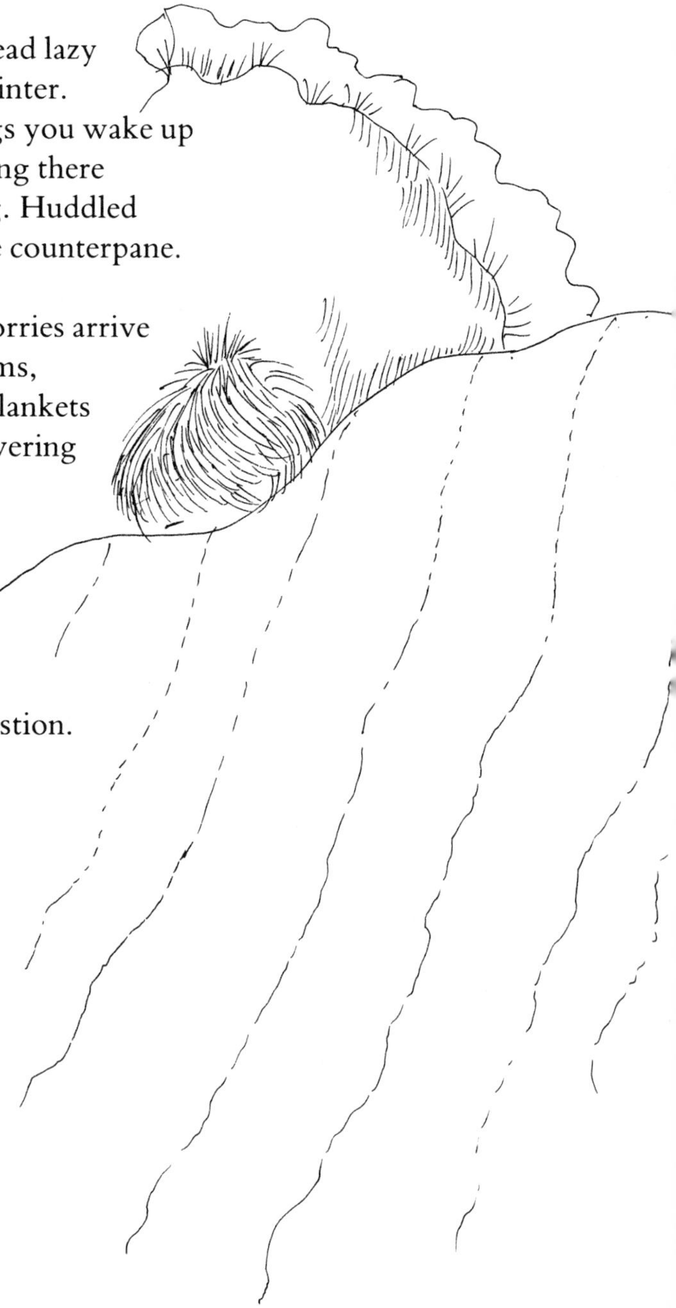

(i)   Our street is dead lazy
      especially in winter.
      Some mornings you wake up
      and it's still lying there
      saying nothing. Huddled
      under its white counterpane.

      But soon the lorries arrive
      like angry mums,
      pull back the blankets
      and send it shivering
      off to work.

(ii) To
      boggan?
      or not
      to boggan?
      That is the question.

(iii) Winter
      morning.
      Snowflakes
      for breakfast.
      The street
      outside
      quiet
      as a
      long
      white
      bandage.

(iv) The time I like best
      is 6 a.m.
      and the snow is six inches deep

      Which I'm yet to discover
      'cos I'm under the cover
      and fast, fast asleep.

ROGER McGOUGH

Reindeer Report

Chimneys: colder.
Flightpaths: busier.
Driver: Christmas (F)
Still baffled by postcodes.

Children: more
And stay up later.
Presents: heavier.
Pay: frozen.

Mission in spite
Of all this
Accomplished.

MERRY CHRISTMAS

U A FANTHORPE

from *The Children of Greene Knowe*

It was late afternoon before they finished the Christmas tree, and it was growing dark. They lit the old red Chinese lantern and many candles so that they could see to work. There were no glaring electric bulbs on this tree. Mrs Oldknow had boxes of coloured glass ornaments, each wrapped separately in tissue paper and put carefully away from year to year. Some were very old and precious indeed. There were glass balls, stars, fircones, acorns and bells in all colours and all sizes. There were also silver medallions of angels. Of course the most beautiful star was fixed at the very top, with gold and silver suns and stars beneath and around it. Each glass treasure, as light as an eggshell and as brittle, was hung on a loop of black cotton that had to be coaxed over the prickly fingers of the tree. Tolly took them carefully out of their tissue paper and Mrs Oldknow hung them up. The tiny glass bell-clappers tinkled when a branch was touched.

When it was all finished, there were no lights on the tree itself, but the candles in the room were reflected in each glass bauble on it, and seemed in those soft deep colours to be shining from an immense distance away, as if the tree were a cloudy night sky full of stars. They sat down together to look at their work. Tolly thought it so beautiful he could say nothing, he could hardly believe his eyes.

As they rested there, tired and dreamy and content, he thought he heard the rocking-horse gently moving, but the sound came from Mrs Oldknow's room, which opened out of the music room. A woman's voice began to sing very softly a cradle song that Tolly had learnt and dearly loved:

> Lully Lulla, Thou little tiny child
> By By, Lully Lullay
> O sisters too, how may we do
> For to preserve this day
> This poor youngling
> For whom we sing
> By by, Lully Lullay

'Who is it?' he whispered.

'It's the grandmother rocking the cradle,' said Mrs Oldknow, and her eyes were full of tears.

'Why are you crying, Granny? It's lovely.'

'It is lovely, only it is such a long time ago. I don't know why that should be sad, but it sometimes seems so.'

The singing began again.

'Granny,' whispered Tolly again, with his arm through hers, 'whose cradle is it? Linnet is as big as I am.'

'My darling, this voice is much older than that. I hardly know whose it is. I heard it once before at Christmas.'

It was queer to hear the baby's sleepy whimper only in the next room, now, and so long ago. 'Come, we'll sing it too,' said Mrs Oldknow, going to the spinet. She played, but it was Tolly who sang alone, while, four hundred years ago, a baby went to sleep.

LUCY M BOSTON

In Beauty May I Walk

In beauty   may I walk
All day long   may I walk
Through the returning seasons may I walk
Beautifully will I possess again
Beautifully birds
Beautifully joyful birds
On the trail marked with pollen may I walk
With grasshoppers about my feet may I walk
With dew about my feet   may I walk
With beauty   may I walk
With beauty before me   may I walk
With beauty behind me   may I walk
With beauty above me   may I walk
With beauty all around me   may I walk
In old age, wandering on a trail of beauty,
       lively, may I walk
In old age, wandering on a trail of beauty,
      living again, may I walk
It is finished in beauty
It is finished in beauty

FROM THE NAVAJO (TRANS. JEROME K ROTHENBERG)

Index of Authors

Anon   15
Auden, W H   96
Baldwin, Marjorie   24
Barker, Cicely Mary   61
BB   26
Binyon, Laurence   98
Boston, Lucy   106
Church, Richard   91
Clark, Elizabeth   54
Clark, Leonard   21, 29, 95
Conan Doyle, Sir Arthur   84
Davies, Idris   71
Dickens, Charles   100
Eytinge, Margaret   64
Fanthorpe, U A   105
Finney, Eric   49
Fisher, Lillian M   103
Foster, John   12, 17
Fyleman, Rose   63
Gibson, Wilfred   68
Grahame, Kenneth   46
Graves, Robert   43
Hardy, Thomas   36
Heaney, Seamus   72
Hoban, Russell   67
Hodgson Burnett, Frances   38
Hopkins, John Henry   10
Housman, A E   31
Hughes, Ted   79
Jennings, Elizabeth   69
Katzin, Olga ('Saggitarius')   80
Larkin, Philip   16
Lee, Laurie   73
McGough, Roger   104

Mackay Brown, George   23
Magee, Wes   8
Matheson, Annie   7
Moore, John   44
Nicholls, Judith   81
Pearce, Philippa   18
Pepys, Samuel   51
Pound, Ezra   101
'Saggitarius' (Olga Katzin)   80
St Luke   17
Scannell, Vernon   96
Sewell, Anna   88
Shakespeare, William   87
Thomas, Dylan   32
Thomas, R S   82
Traditional   92
Wade, Barrie   83
Wilson, Raymond   66
Wordsworth, William   76
Young, Andrew   53

Acknowledgements

The editor and the Publisher would like to thank the following for their kind permission to reprint copyright material in this book:

'Elegy for JFK' by W H Auden from *About the House*, reprinted by permission of Faber and Faber Ltd; Methuen Children's Books for the extract from *The Little Grey Men* by BB (Methuen); Frederick Warne & Co for 'Song of the Scarlet Pimpernel Fairy' by Cicely Mary Barker, copyright © the estate of Cicely Mary Barker 1925, 1944. Reproduced by permission of Frederick Warne & Co; the Society of Authors and Mrs Nicolete Gray on behalf of the Laurence Binyon Estate for 'For the Fallen (September 1914)' by Laurence Binyon; the extract from *The Children of Green Knowe* by Lucy M Boston, reprinted by permission of Faber and Faber Ltd; Laurence Pollinger Ltd and the Estate of Richard Church for 'The Alchemist' by Richard Church from *Collected Poems*; Hodder and Stoughton Publishers for the extract from *The Tale of a Tail* by Elizabeth Clark; Dobson Books Ltd for 'First Primrose' and 'In March' by Leonard Clark from *Good Company* (Dobson Books); Robert A Clarke, Literary Executor for Leonard Clark for 'Daffodils'; 'High Summer on the Mountains' by Iris Davies from *Selected Poems* (Faber), reprinted by permission of Faber and Faber Ltd; Peterloo Poets for 'Reindeer Report' by U A Fanthorpe from *Standing To*; Eric Finney for 'Mystery Story' from *A Very First Poetry Book* (Oxford University Press) by Eric Finney; Harper & Row (New York) for 'A Season' by Lillian M Fisher from *More Surprises* ed. Lee Bennett Hopkins (1987); John Foster for 'Giant Winter' and 'The Invaders' by John Foster from *Another Fourth Poetry Book* (Puffin); The Society of Authors as the Literary Representatives of the Estate of Rose Fyleman for 'The Balloon Man' by Rose Fyleman; Mr Michael Gibson and Macmillan, London and Basingstoke, for 'The Ice' by Wilfred Gibson from *Collected Poems*; A P Watt Ltd on behalf of the Trustees of the Robert Graves Copyright Trust for 'Flying Crooked' from *Collected Poems* (Cassells 1975); 'Blackberry Picking' by Seamus Heaney from *Death of a Naturalist* reprinted by permission of Faber and Faber Ltd; David Higham Associates for 'School Buses' by Russell Hoban from *Six of the Best: A Puffin Sextet* (Puffin); 'Fox' by Ted Hughes from *What is the Truth?*, reprinted by permission of Faber and Faber Ltd; David Higham Associates for 'Holidays at Home' by Elizabeth Jennings from *The Secret Brother* (Macmillan); Jonathan Cape Ltd for 'Nerves (2 September 1939)' by Olga Katzin from *Saggitarius Rhyming*; 'First Sight' by Philip Larkin from *The Whitsun Weddings* reprinted by permission of Faber and Faber Ltd; the Hogarth Press for the extract from *Cider With Rosie* by Laurie Lee; Wes Magee for 'A New Clear Winter' by Wes Magee; John Murray Publishers for 'Beachcomber' by George MacKay Brown from *Fishermen With Ploughs*; Peters Fraser and Dunlop Group Ltd for 'Snow and Ice Poems' by Roger McGough from *Sky in the Pie* (Viking/Kestrel); Peters Fraser and Dunlop Group Ltd for the extract from *Brensham Village* (1966) by John Moore; 'Harvest Hymn' by Judith Nicholls from *Dragonsfire*, reprinted by permission of Faber and Faber Ltd; the extract from *Tom's Midnight Garden* © Oxford University Press 1958. Reprinted from *Tom's Midnight Garden* by A Philippa Pearce

(1958) by permission of Oxford University Press; 'Ancient Music' by Ezra Pound from *Lustra*, reprinted by permission of Faber and Faber Ltd; Vernon Scannell for 'Gunpowder Plot' by Vernon Scannell; J M Dent & Sons Ltd for the extract from *Under Milk Wood* by Dylan Thomas; R S Thomas, 53 Gloucester Rd, Kew, UK, for 'A Day in Autumn' © R S Thomas from *Poetry for Supper* (Rupert Hart Davies Publishers Ltd 1958); Alison Young, Literary Executor of Andrew Young for 'The Swallows' by Andrew Young from *The Poetical Works of Andrew Young* ed. Lowbury and Young (Secker & Warburg); 'Conkers' © Barrie Wade 1989, reprinted by permission of Oxford University Press; Raymond Wilson for 'The Lighthouse' by Raymond Wilson.

Every effort has been made to trace the copyright holders but the editor and the Publisher apologise if any inadvertent omission has been made.